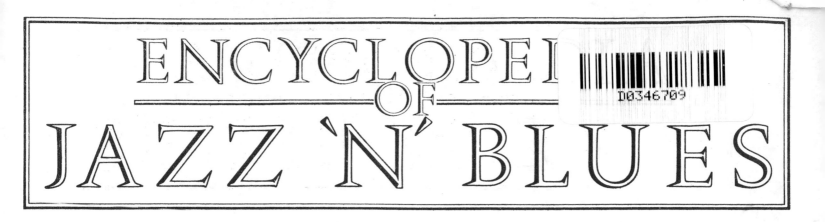

ENCYCLOPEDIA OF JAZZ 'N' BLUES

Front cover photograph courtesy of
BBC Hulton Picture Library

Edited & Arranged by
CECIL BOLTON & CHRIS ELLIS
First Published 1988
© EMI Music Publishing Ltd
138 Charing Cross Road, London WC2H 0LD

Exclusive Distributors
International Music Publications
Southend Road, Woodford Green,
Essex IG8 8HN, England.

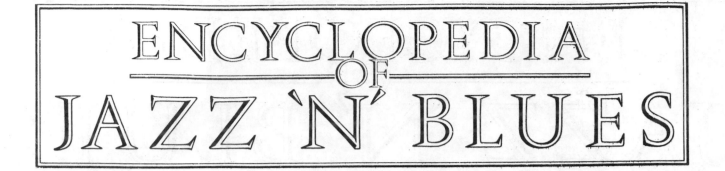

ENCYCLOPEDIA OF JAZZ 'N' BLUES

After You've Gone

Words and Music by
TURNER LAYTON and HENRY CREAMER

*Alternative couplet: Some day, when you grow lonely,
        Your heart will break like mine and you'll want me only,

Aintcha Got Music?

Words by ANDY RAZAF
Music by J. JOHNSON

CHORUS

9

Alabama Blues

New Words and Music by
CHRIS ELLIS, CECIL BOLTON & MARTIN LITTON

I'm Alabama bound
I'm Alabama bound
Said if the train don't stop and turn around
I'm Alabama bound.

Oh don't you leave me here
Said don't you leave me here
But.if you're bound to go sweet lovin' babe
Leave me a dime for beer.

I went to bed last night
The blues were all around
I heard a bed bug in the corner sing
I'm Alabama bound.

My baby left me flat
And she just can't be found
So now you know the reason why I say
I'm Alabama bound.

I'm singing in the cold
Passin' my hat around
And if I make enough to pay the fare
I'm Alabama bound.

I'm Alabama bound
I'm Alabama bound
Said if the train don't stop and turn around
I'm Alabama bound.

All The Wrongs You've Done To Me

Words and Music by
EDGAR DOWELL, LEW PAYTON and CHRIS SMITH

Moderato

VERSE

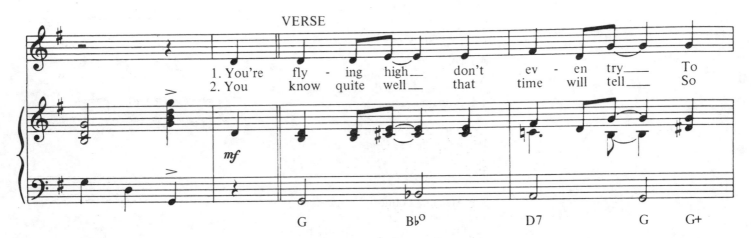

1. You're fly - ing high____ don't ev - en try____ To
2. You know quite well____ that time will tell____ So

G   Bb°   D7   G   G+

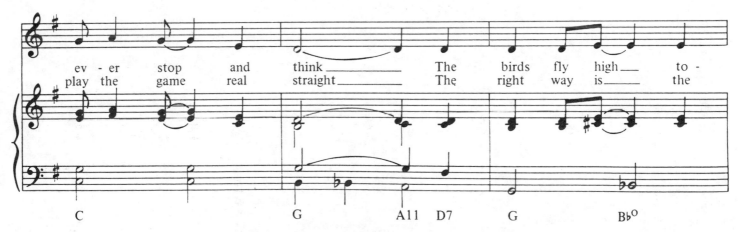

ev - er stop and think_____ The birds fly high____ to -
play the game real straight_____ The right way is____ the

C   G   A11 D7   G   Bb°

wards the sky____ But they've got to come down____ and drink_____
on - ly way____ it is best not to fool____ with fate._____

D7   G   F#   Bm Bb° D7

A Sunday Kind Of Love

Words and Music by
BARBARA BELLE, ANITA LEONARD, STAN RHODES and LOUIS PRIMA

At The Animals Ball

New Words and Music by
CHRIS ELLIS and CECIL BOLTON

20

At the An - i - mals Ball.   2. Now the   at   the   An - i - mals

Gm7   C7   F   C7   G7   Gm7/C

Ball. _____

F   B♭m6   F

2. Now the Lion came to the door
    They knew that he was sore
    He said "Let me in this hall
    Or I'll break-up your doggone ball.
    Can't you see I want to prance
    And I mean to take a chance"
    He gave a roar, broke down the door
    That was the end of the dance.

Chorus:

    Now the Chimps were Skrontching back to back
    The big Gorilla Balled the Jack
    The Hippo being up to date
    Did the Shimmy-sha-Wobble like Sister Kate.
    The Eagle did the Eagle Rock
    And the Viper did the Crawl.
    Way down in the Jungle
    At the Animal's Ball. I mean
    Way down in the Jungle
    At that Animal's Ball.

Baltimore Oriole

Words by PAUL FRANCIS WEBSTER
Music by HOAGY CARMICHAEL

Basin St. Blues

Words and Music by SPENCER WILLIAMS

CHORUS

Big Bad Bill

(Is Sweet William Now)

Words by JACK YELLEN
Music by MILTON AGER

Mar-ried life has changed __ him some-how _____ He's the

G
G7

man that they all used to fear; _____ Now the peo-ple call him Wil-lie dear. ____ He was

C   G+   C   Cm   G   E7

strong-er than Sam-son, I de-clare,__Till a home town De-lil-ah bobbed his hair. __

A7   D7

Big Bad Bill don't fight __ an-y more; _____

G   D   D7+   G   Gm   D7

Boodle Am – Shake

Words and Music by
JACK PALMER and SPENCER WILLIAMS

Bye Bye Blues

Words and Music by
DAVE BENNETT and FRED HAMM

CHORUS

Bye Bye Blues,_____ Bye Bye Blues._____

Bb Gb   Bb G7

Bells ring, birds sing, Sun is shin-ing,

C7   F F9 Dm Bb Db°

No more pin-ing. Just we two_____ Smil

Cm7 F7 Cm7 F7+ Bb Gb Bb

ing through._____ Don't sigh, Don't cry,

G7   C9 F7

1.   2.

Bye Bye Blues._____ Blues._____

Bb Gb Bb Eb7 E7 F7 Bb Eb7 Bb

Can't We Be Friends

Words by PAUL JAMES
Music by KAY SWIFT

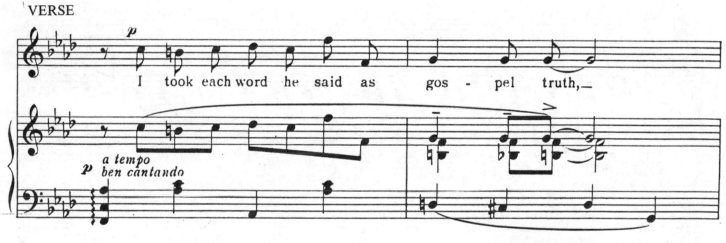

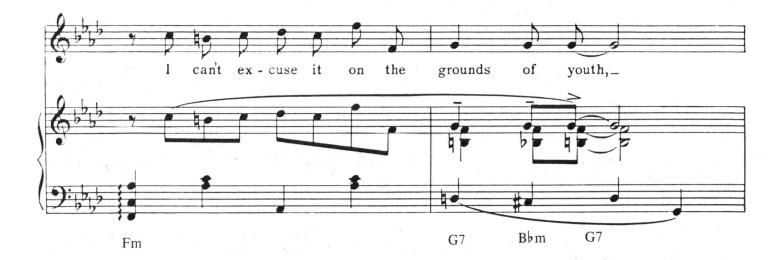

I can't ex-cuse it on the grounds of youth,_

Fm   G7   B♭m   G7

I was no babe in the wild wood.   He did-n't mean it, _

C7   F   B♭   F   B♭m   Fm

I should have seen it, _   Now___ it's too late!

G7   F   C+   F   C   A♭7

38

Can't We Talk It Over?

Words by NED WASHINGTON
Music by VICTOR YOUNG

Cherokee

Words & Music by RAY NOBLE

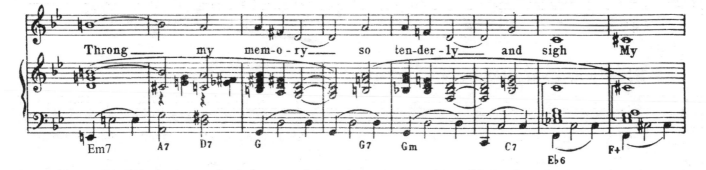

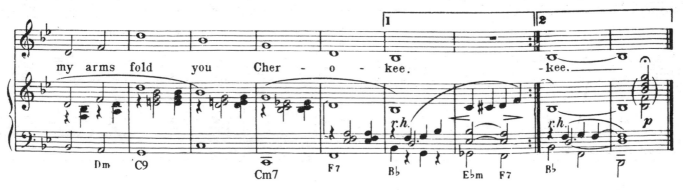

Come Rain Or Come Shine

Words by JOHNNY MERCER
Music by HAROLD ARLEN

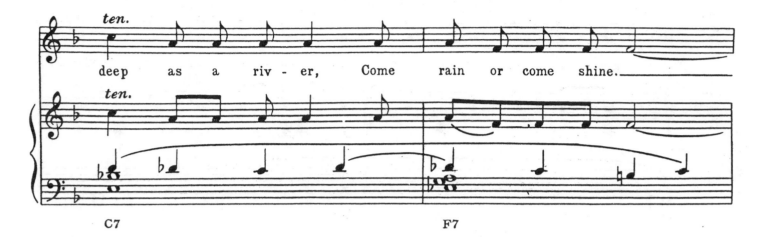

deep as a riv - er, Come rain or come shine._____

C7   F7

— I guess when you met me It was

molto espr.

G♭   Cm7   F7   B♭m   Fm

just one of those things, But don't ev - er

B♭m   C7(♭5)   Fm

bet me, 'Cause I'm gon - na be true if you let me.

mf dim   *rit*

E♭m   Adim   Fdim   C7   B♭dim   Cdim   G7   G7(♭5)   C9

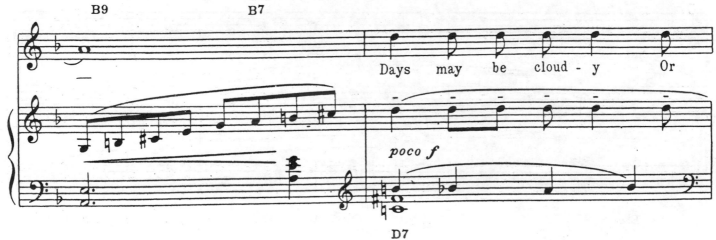

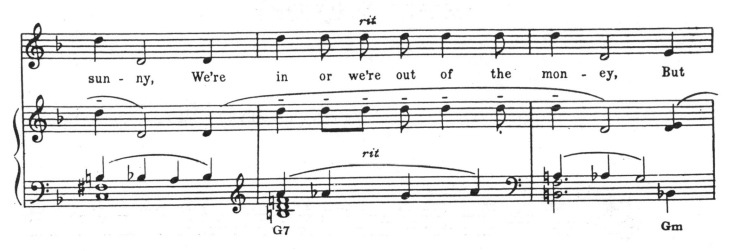

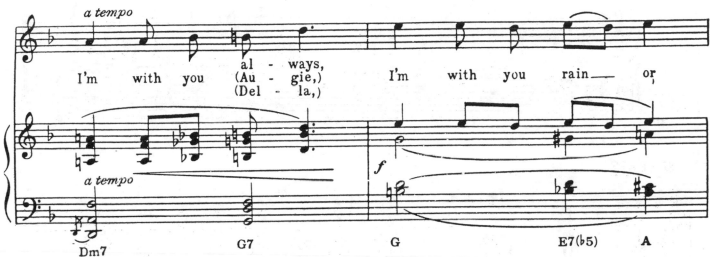

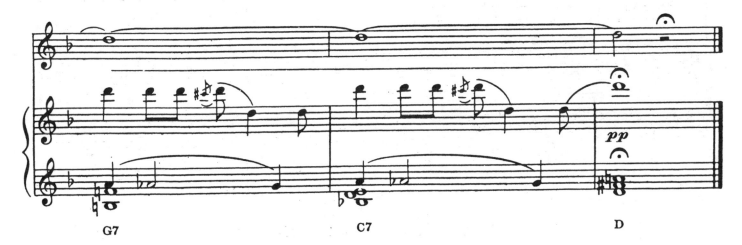

Crazy Rhythm

Words by IRVING CAESAR
Music by JOSEPH MEYER and ROGER WOLFE KAHN

Moderato

𝄋 VERSE

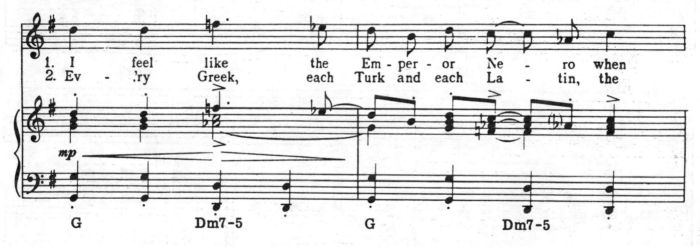

1. I feel like the Em-per-or Ne - ro when
2. Ev - 'ry Greek, each Turk and each La - tin, the

G   Dm7-5   G   Dm7-5

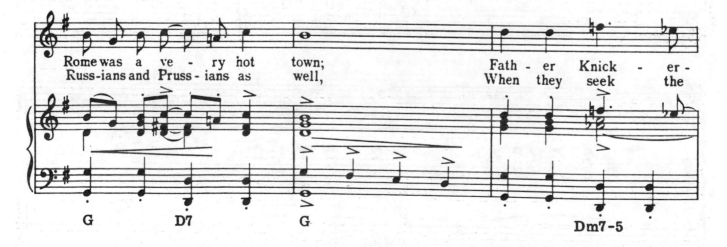

Rome was a ve - ry hot town;
Russ-ians and Pruss-ians as well,

Fath - er Knick - er -
When they seek the

G   D7   G   Dm7-5

CHORUS

Cra - zy Rhy - thm, here's the door-way, I'll go my way, you'll go your way!

Gmaj9 G6 Gmaj7 G6 Gmaj9 G6 Gmaj7 G6

Cra - zy Rhythm, from now on_we're through._____ Here is where we

D7 Am7 D7 Am7 G6 G Gmaj9 G6
D7

have a show-down, I'm too high-hat, you're too low-down. Cra - zy Rhy - thm,

Gmaj7 G6 Gmaj9 G6 Gmaj7 G6 D7 Am7

here's goodbye to you!_____ They say that when a high-brow meets a low-brow

D7 Am7 G6 D7 G7 Dm7 G7 Dm7
D7 G7

The Darktown Strutters' Ball

Words and Music by
SHELTON BROOKS

1. I've got some good news, Hon-ey, An in-vi-ta-tion to the
2. We'll meet our high-toned neigh-bours, An ex-hi-bi-tion of the

Dark-town Ball, It's a ve-ry swell af fair,_____ All the
"Ba-by Dolls," And each one will do their best,_____ Just to

"High browns" will be there,___ I'll wear my high silk hat and a
out - class all the rest,___ And there'll be danc - ers from ev - 'ry

Am   Cm6   D7   G   D7   G7   C   Cdim

frock tail coat   You wear your Par - is gown and your new silk shawl, There
for - eign land,   The class - ic, buck and wing, and the wood - en clog: We'll

Dm7   G7   E7   Am   E7   Am   Gdim

ain't no doubt a - bout it, babe, We'll be the best dressed in the hall.___
win that fif - ty dol - lar prize, When we step out and "Walk the Dog!"___

G   Gm   B7   Em   E7   Am   D7   G

CHORUS

I'll be down to get you in a Tax - i, Hon - ey, You bet-ter be read - y a-bout half past eight,

mf

C   A7   D7

Now dear-ie, don't be late, I want to be there when the band starts play-ing. Re-
-mem-ber when we get there, Hon-ey, The two-steps, I'm goin' to have 'em all, Goin' to
dance out both my shoes,— When they play the "Jel-ly Roll Blues," To-

-mor-row night at the Dark-town Strutters' Ball. _____ I'll be —

Darn That Dream

Words by EDDIE DE LANGE
Music by JAMES VAN HEUSEN

Slowly

Love is a strange and pow-er-ful thing, It can bring you down, or

Eb   Cm7 Fm7   Bb7 Bb7+ G7(5b)   C9

make you sing.   Love may give you a mil-lion-aire's scheme, But it

F7(5b)   Bb9   Eb   Cm7   G9#7   G6

on-ly gave me one dream.   Darn that dream I dream each night, You

Em7   A7   Am7   D79b   G Eb7   Am7   B75# B7

say you love me and you hold me tight, But when I a-wake, you're out of sight, Oh

Em   Am   Dm6   E7   Am7   F9   Bm7   B♭o   E♭7

darn that dream! Darn your lips and darn your eyes, They

Am7+4   A♭7   G   Am7 D7(9♭) G   E♭7   Am7   B75♯   B7

lift me high a-bove the moon-lit skies, Then I tum-ble out of par - a - dise, Oh

Em   Am   Dm6   E7   Am7   F9   Bm7   B♭o   E♭7

darn that dream! Darn that one track mind of mine, It

Am7   A♭7   G   B♭7   E♭   Cm   Fm7   B♭7

'Deed I Do

Words and Music by
WALTER HIRSCH and FRED ROSE

CHORUS

Diga Diga Doo

Words by DOROTHY FIELDS
Music by JIMMY McHUGH

CHORUS

I'm so ver-y Di-ga Di-ga Doo by na-ture, _____ If you don't say

D7   G   C7   B7   E7

Di-ga Di-ga to your mate you're Gon-na lose a Pa-pa; So Let those fun-ny
No - one heeds the

Am   B7   F7   Em   G+

peo-ple smile, How can there be a Vir-gin Isle With Di-ga Di-ga Doo Di-ga
mar-riage laws, Yours is mine and mine is yours

Em   A7   Em   G+   Em7   A7   Em   B7

1. | **2. to Patter** | **Last**

Doo Doo, Di-ga Di-ga Doo Di-ga Doo. Doo. Doo. *Fine.*

Em   B7   Em   B7   Em   B7   Em

Don't Be Angry With Me

Words and Music by
WALTER DONALDSON

VERSE

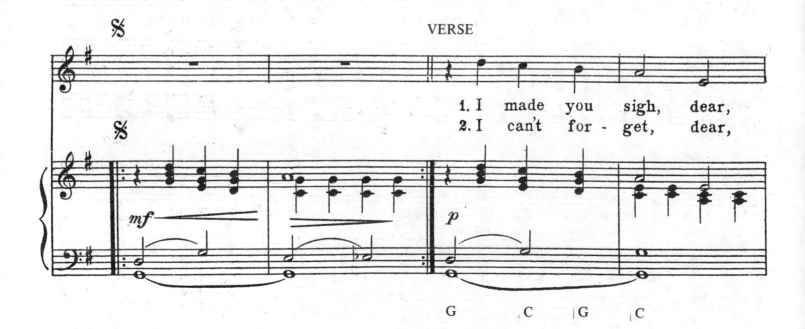

1. I made you sigh, dear,
2. I can't for - get, dear,

CHORUS *2nd time* **f**

Don't be_____ an - gry____

G   Ab

an - gry___ with me,_____ I did - n't mean____

G   E   A7

to make you feel so blue, I did - n't mean____ to be so

D13   G   Gm

mean to you. Come on and let's be_____

Am7   D7   G

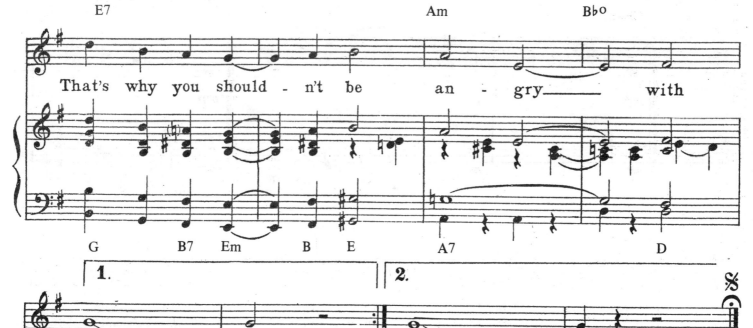

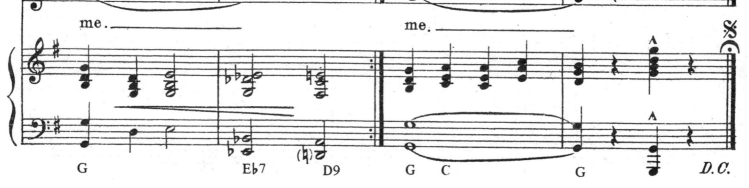

Down Hearted Blues

Words by ALBERTA HUNTER
Music by LOVIE AUSTIN

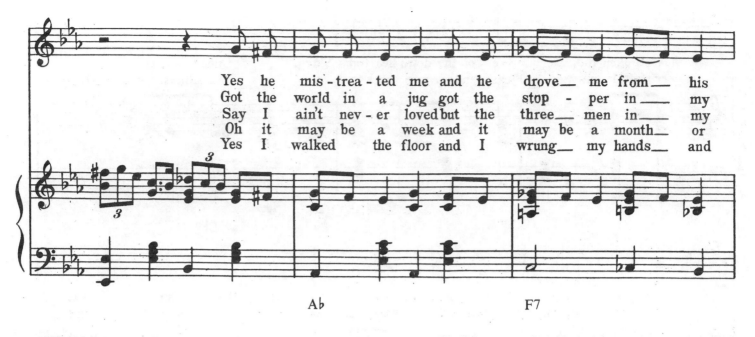

Yes he mis-trea-ted me and he drove___ me from___ his
Got the world in a jug got the stop-per in___ my
Say I ain't nev-er loved but the three men in___ my
Oh it may be a week and it may be a month___ or
Yes I walked the floor and I wrung___ my hands___ and

Ab   F7

door,   But the good book says you'll reap___ just what___ you
hand   And if you want me you must come un-der my___ com-
life,   'Twas my fath-er, brother and the man___ who wrecked my
two,   All the dirt you did to me will come home___ to
cried,   Had the down hearted blues and could-n't be sat - is -

Eb   Bb7   F7   Eb

1   **2**
sow.   Got the   sow
-mand.   Say I   -mand.
life.   Oh, it   life.
you.   Oh, I   you.
-fied.   -fied.

Eb   F7   Bb   Eb   Bb7   Eb

Easy Living

Words and Music by
LEO ROBIN and RALPH RAINGER

Molto Moderato (*Dreamily*)

Voice

Liv-ing for you, Is eas-y liv-ing It's

Eb   Edim   Fm   Bb7

eas-y to live When you're in love__ and I'm so in love, there's

Eb   Cm   Ab   Abm   Eb   C7

noth-ing in life__ but you._____   I

Fm   Bb9   Bb+9   Eb   Edim   Fm7   Bb9   Bb+9

nev-er re-gret the years I'm giv-ing They're eas-y to give

Eb   Edim   Fm   Bb7   Eb   Cm

When you're in love___ I'm hap-py to do what-ev-er I do___ for

Ab   Abm   Eb   C7   Fm   Bb9   Ddim

you___ for you

Eb   Ab   Eb   Ab   Eb   Cb

May-be I'm a fool___ but it's fun.___ Peo-ple say you rule me with one___

Gb7   Cb   Gb7

wave of your hand— Dar - ling it's grand— They

Cb   Abm   Bb7sus   Bb7   Fm7

cresc. poco - a - poco - - - -

just don't un-der - stand. Liv - ing for you Is eas - y liv - ing, It's

Bb7   Eb   Edim   Fm   Bb7

Bb+9

mf - f

eas-y to live When you're in love and I'm so in love There's noth-ing in life but

Eb   Cm   Ab   Abm   Eb   C7   Fm   Bb9   Ddim

you.   you.

rit.

Eb   Fm   Eb   B9   Bb7sus   Bb7   Bb+7   Eb   Fm   Eb   Ab   Eb   Bb+9   Eb

Emaline

Words by MITCHELL PARISH
Music by FRANK PERKINS

to me-an-der with me, Have you told your friends, Have you told your peo-ple,

F Gm7 F#o C+ F Cm D7

EM-A-LINE?__ Hur-ry up and write them a line__ 'Bout a wed-din' to be, In the

G7 C+ C7 F G7 B♭o F

church there's an old bell ring-er,__ Just wait-in' for the time, When I place a ring a-round your fin-ger,

B♭m7 E♭7 A♭ B♭m7 E♭7 Cm Dm G7(♭9) C E♭o

mak-in' you mine, All I do is pray for that Sunday mornin' sun to shine,__ When I prom-en-ade

Dm7 G7 C11 C7 F Cm D7 G7

down the line__ Hand in hand with EM-A-LINE. -LINE.

C+ Gm7 C7 F F#o Gm7 F D♭7 C7 F F#o C+ F

G#o Gm7

Farewell Blues

Words and Music by
LEON ROPOLLO, PAUL MARES and ELMER SCHOEBEL

Slowly

VERSE

Sad - ness just makes me

G   D7

sigh _____ I've come to say good-bye _____

G   Em7   G   D7   G

Al - - tho'   I   go

Em7   E7   Am   Eb7

I've   got those fare-well blues _____

G   D   Eo D7   G

CHORUS
Mysterioso

Those Fare - well blues make me yearn

G7

That part - ing kiss seems to burn

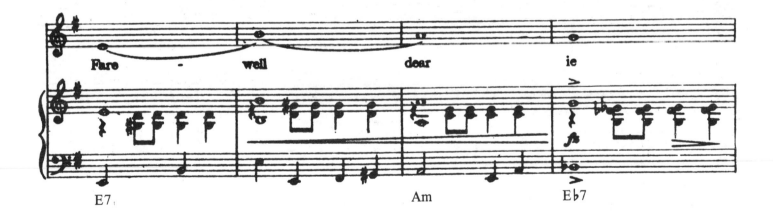

Fare - well dear ie

E7 Am E♭7

Some - - - - day I will re - turn.

G7 G#° D7

Dream ing of you is sweet _____

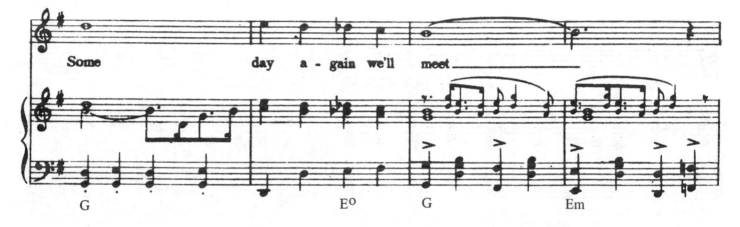

Some day a - gain we'll meet _____

My fears for years

were those sad fare - well blues. _____

Fat & Greasy

Words and Music by
P. GRAINGER and C. JOHNSON

Blues Tempo
VERSE

There is a fel-low who — I'm tell-in' you, — he's big as two; —

He's to darned la-zy to reach down and tie his shoe;

He weighs a third of a ton — This big fat son of a gun; —

Talk 'bout your lais-sez faire, — He's too in-ert to care.

82

Inter-Choruses (after each chorus)

Watch him while he's sit-tin' there,_ Chunks of fat hang from his chair,_

Bb   Bb7   Eb   Ebo   Bb   Dbo   Cm7   F7

Oil just ooz-in' from his hair,_ Fat and greas-y as a bear._

Bb   Bb7   E7   Ebo   Bb   Eb7   Bb   Dbo   Cm7   F7   Bb   F7

CHORUS

Man, that fool is Fat an' greas-y, Hot or cool he's Fat an' greas-y,

Bb   Bb7   Eb   Ebo   Bb   Dbo   Cm7   F7

1-8   D.C.

Head to heel he's Fat an' greas-y Big fat greas-y fool._

Bb   Eb   Bb7   Eb   Ebo   Bb   Gb7   F7   Bb   D.C.   Bb

2. Sweet perfumes are made from fat,
    But not from this greasy cat;
    There's a fragrance in his clothes
    But 'tain't like what's in a rose.

3. Since he don't use Mum's nor Hush,
    He would make a pole-cat blush,
    And I don't care how he's dress,
    He would be a big fat mess.

4. He's got big fat liver lips,
    Shakes like jelly 'round his hips,
    He's a waddlin', wigglin' shame
    With a big fat what's-his-name.

5. When he squeezes thru' the door,
    Wood starts creakin' in the floor,
    What he calls a gentle snore
    Sounds more like a lion's roar.

6. He don't know no etiquette
    And ain't in no smarter set,
    He'll eat anything in sight,
    Then haul off and snore all night.

7. He don't often socialise,
    'Cause of his gigantic size,
    He don't class with folks elite'
    Just cause he don't smell so sweet.

8. He don't neither spin nor toil,
    He just sets and oozes oil,
    Get in ten feet of this cat, (he'll)
    Chloroform you quick as that (snap).

9. In his manner he's as mild
    As a harmless little child,
    Big fat worthless, greasy chap,
    You can't help but like the sap.

The Flat Foot Floogee

Words and Music by
SLIM GAILLARD, SLAM STEWART and BUD GREEN

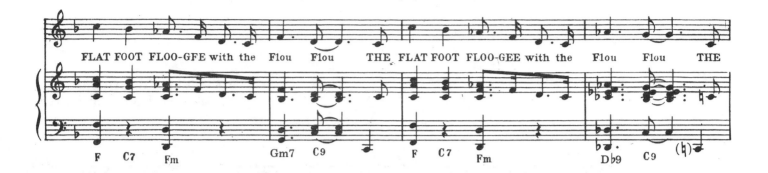

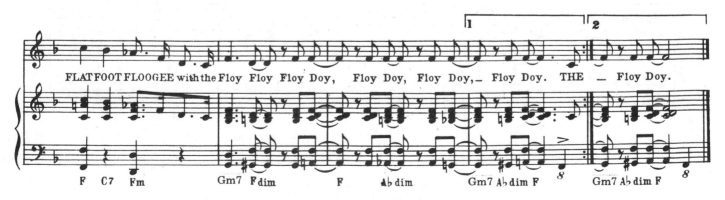

Fine And Dandy

Words by PAUL JAMES
Music by KAY SWIFT

Gee Baby, Ain't I Good To You

Words by ANDY RAZAF & DON REDMAN
Music by DON REDMAN

INTERLUDE

Lis-ten,— lis-ten to what I have to say,— what I want to tell you,

Lis-ten,— lis-ten to why I feel this way,— just why I feel this way,—

Say do you ev-er won-der, just why I'm nev-er blue?

Say do you ev-er won-der, just why I'm so good to you.—

D. S. to Chorus

Get Happy

Words and Music by
HAROLD ARLEN and TED KOEHLER

head - in' 'cross the Riv - er,— wash your sins 'way in the tide. It's

Ab7   Db7   C7+ F7   Bb7

all so peace - ful on the oth - er side___ For-get your trou-bles and just get

Ab7   Db7   C7   F7   Bb7   Eb   Bb7 Cm

hap-py___ You bet-ter chase all your cares a - way_____ Shout Hal-le - lu-jah! come on, get

Eb6 Bb7   Eb   Eb6   Bb7   Ab ·   Eb   Eb6   Bb7 Cm
                              Cm

1

2

hap-py___ Get read - y for the judge-ment day.   For-get your day.___

Eb6   Bb7   Eb   Bb7   Eb Cb7 Bb7 Eb   Eb
    Ebm

Fine

The Girl Across The Hall

Words by CHARLOTTE STEINHART
Music by BRENDA COOPER & NOEL HENDRICK

Chorus 2:

I ain't sewin' on your buttons, I ain't cleanin' up your mess
And when I tell you 'no' man I won't be meanin' 'yes'
I won't be comin' when you call
I'm gonna stay across the hall.
You've been takin' me for granted now you know what you can do
'Cos I'm here to say with feelin' that I've had enough of you
I'm out to have myself a ball
With someone else across the hall.
What did I see in you?
How could love have been quite so blind?
I was crazy about you
But now it's heaven without you.
Wastin' no more tears upon you, this is where I start to live
'Cos this guy I've found is wild about the things I've got to give
When you don't have no one at all
You'll miss the girl across the hall.

Goodbye Blues

Words and Music by
DOROTHY FIELDS, JIMMY McHUGH and ARNOLD JOHNSON

100

Chorus. *(slow with feeling)*

Lone - - some nights,_____ Low

Eb   Bbdim   Bb7

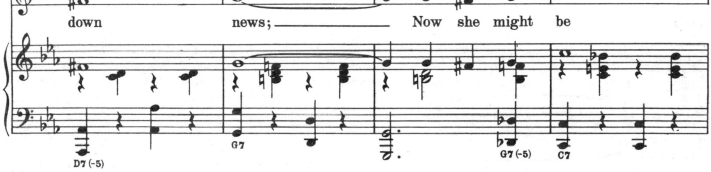

down news;_____ Now she might be

D7(-5)   G7   G7(-5)   C7

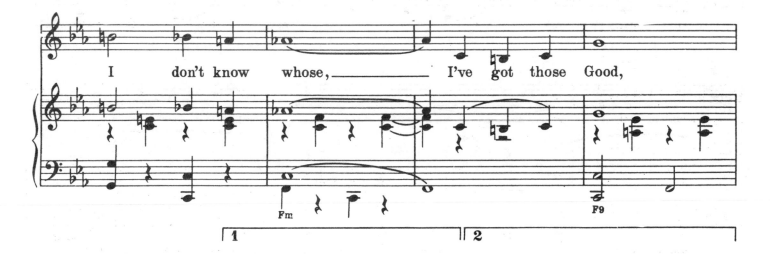

I don't know whose,_____ I've got those Good,

Fm   F9

1   2

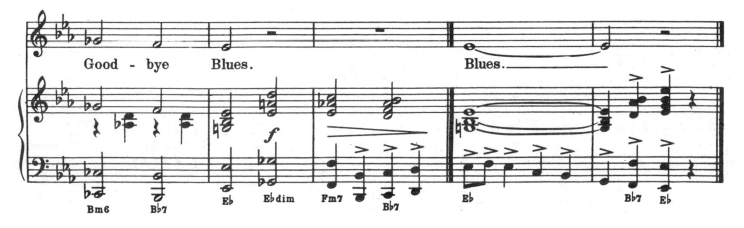

Good - bye Blues.   Blues._____

Bm6   Bb7   Eb   Ebdim   Fm7   Bb7   Eb   Bb7   Eb

The Gypsy In My Soul

Words by MOE JAFFE and CLAY BOLAND
Music by CLAY BOLAND

VERSE

CHORUS

If I am fan-cy free, And love to wan - der, It's just the

gyp-sy in my soul.___ There's some-thing call-ing me,___

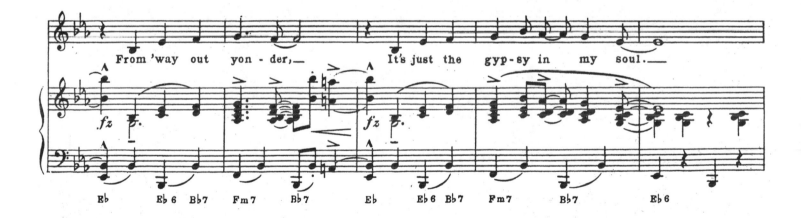

From 'way out yon - der,___ It's just the gyp-sy in my soul.___

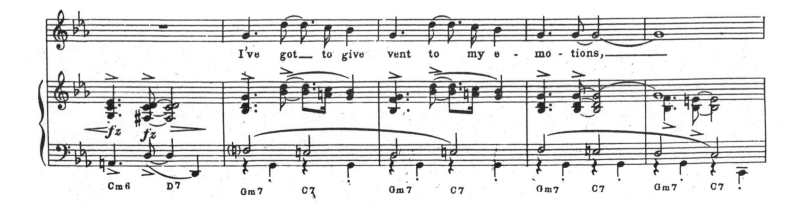

I've got___ to give vent to my e - mo - tions,___

I'm on-ly con-tent hav-ing my way._____ There is no oth-er life_

Of which I'm fond-er,_ It's just the gyp-sy in my soul_____ No cares,

No strings._____ My heart_____ has wings.

If I am fan-cy free, And love to wan-der,

It's just the gyp-sy in_ my soul._

I Gotta Right To Sing The Blues

Words by TED KOEHLER
Music by HAROLD ARLEN

REFRAIN

Slowly and with much expression

I got-ta right to sing the blues _____ I got-ta right to feel low-down _____

C7   F

I got-ta right to hang a-round, ___ down a-round the riv -

F7   Bb   *appassionato*

-er, ___ A cer-tain man in this old town _____ Keeps draggin' my poor heart a-round.

G7   C7   F Eb7 Eb E

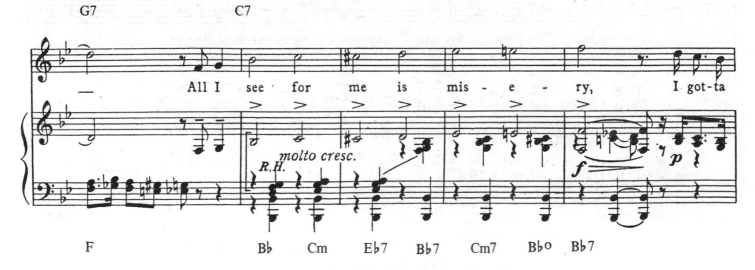

All I see for me is mis - e - ry, ___ I got-ta

F   Bb Cm Eb7 Bb7 Cm7 Bb° Bb7

molto cresc.

R.H.

right to sing the blues _____ I got-ta right to moan and sigh _____ I got-ta

C7   F7

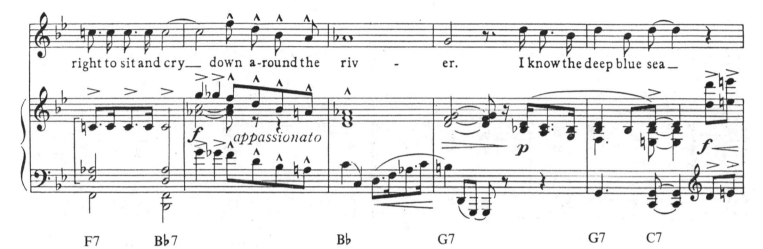

right to sit and cry ___ down a-round the riv - er. I know the deep blue sea ___

appassionato

F7   Bb7   Bb   G7   G7   C7

Will soon be call-ing me.___ It must be love - say what you choose, I

Eb   Gm7   C7

got-ta right to sing the blues._____ I got-ta _____

Ebm6   F13   Bᵒ   Bb

morendo

Have You Ever Felt That Way?

Words and Music by
AGNES CASTLETON and SPENCER WILLIAMS

Hot Lips

Words and Music by
HENRY BUSSE, HENRY LANGE and LOU DAVIS

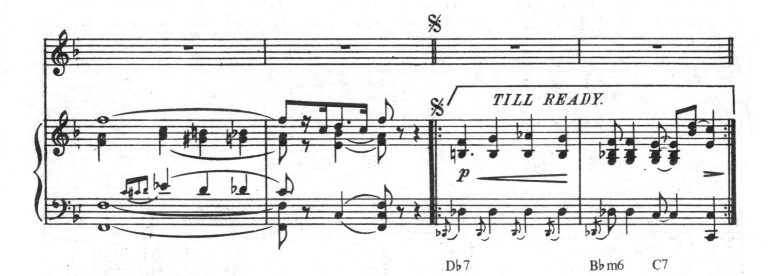

1. There's a boy that's in our band — And how he blows that
2. Heard him play the oth-er night, And old man Os-car

horn,_____ Fin - est since you're born,_____
Clive _____ Who is eight - y - five _____

C7

When he starts you're gone _____ They all call him
Sure as you're a - live _____ Got so frisk - y

F   Db7

"Hot Lips" for ___ He blows real red - hot notes, _____ And
when he start - ed out to do his stuff, _____ Was

F   Eb°

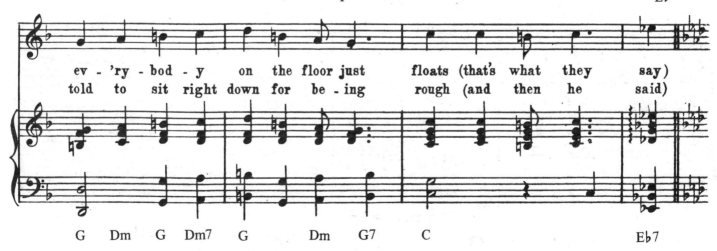

ev - 'ry - bod - y on the floor just floats (that's what they say)
told to sit right down for be - ing rough (and then he said)

G Dm G Dm7 G Dm G7 C   Eb7

CHORUS. *2nd time* **f**

He's got hot lips ———— When he plays Jazz, ———— He draws out

Eb+   Ab6   Bo   Eb7

steps ———— Like no one has ———— You're on your toes,

Eb+   Ab   Eb+   Ab6

——— And shake your shoes ———————— Boy, how he goes ———

B   Eb   Bb+   Eb   F#o   Bb7

——When he plays Blues! ————————— I watch the crowd ———

Bb7+   Eb   Eb+   Ab6

Un - til he's thro', _____ He can be proud _____ They're "cue - koo,"

B⁰   Eb7   Eb+

too _____ His mu - sic's rare, You must de -

Ab7 Bbm B7⁰ Ab7   Bb7 E7 Ab   C7   C7(b5)

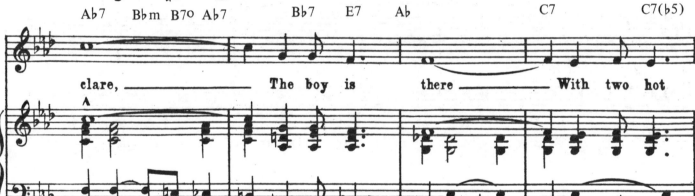

clare, _____ The boy is there _____ With two hot

Fm   Bb7 B7⁰ Ab B⁰   Eb7

1.   2.   %

lips. _____ He's got hot lips. _____

Fine.

D.C.

Ab   Eb+   Ab   Eb7 A

How High The Moon

Words by NANCY HAMILTON
Music by MORGAN LEWIS

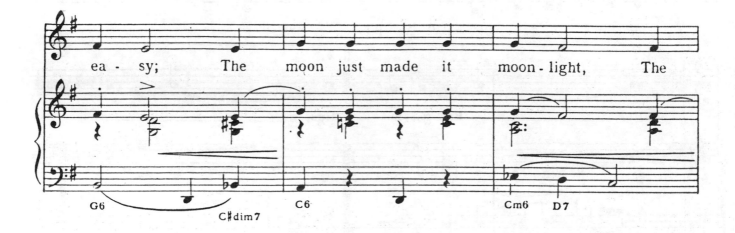

breeze just made it bree - zy, And then I

fell in love, And things that once were clear

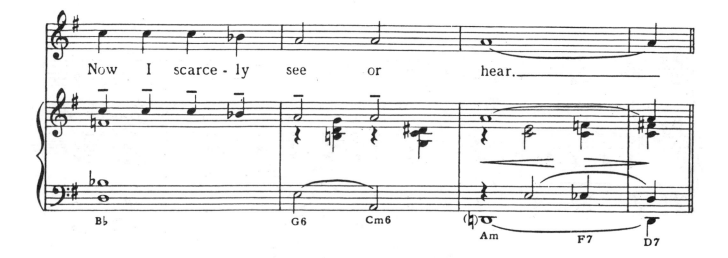

Now I scarce - ly see or hear._____

(Slowly, with expression)

Some-where there's mu - sic,____ How faint the tune!____

____ Some-where there's hea - ven,____ How high the moon!____ There is no

moon a - bove When love is far_ a - way, too,_____ Till it comes

true_____ That you love me as I love you. Some-where there's

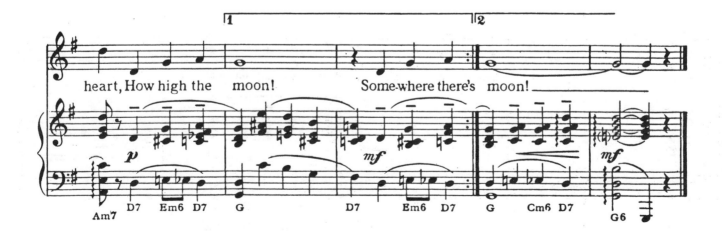

I Cover The Waterfront

Words and Music by
JOHN W. GREEN

REFRAIN (*Not fast*)

Ida! Sweet As Apple Cider

Words by EDDIE MUNSON
Music by EDDIE LEONARD

CHORUS

I - da! ___ Sweet as ap-ple ci - der, ___ Sweet - er ___ than all I

know ___ Come out! ___ In the sil-v'ry moon - light ___ Of love we'll whis - per ___

___ so soft and low! Seems I ___ can't live with - out ___ you. ___

Lis - ten ___ Oh! hon-ey do! ___ I - da! ___ I I I-do-lize yer,

I love you I - da 'deed I do. ___ do. ___

I Double Dare You

Words and Music by
TERRY SHAND and JIMMY EATON

I Hear Music

Words by FRANK LOESSER
Music by BURTON LANE

rat-tle of the milk-man on the stair. Sure that's mu - sic Might-y fine mu - sic, The

sing-ing of a spar-row in the sky, the perk-ing of the cof-fee right near-by. There's my fav -'rite

mel - o - dy You my an - gel phon-ing me.___

I hear mu - sic, Might-y fine mu - sic And an-y-time I think my world is wrong, I

get me out of bed and sing___ this song.___ song.

I'll Never Be The Same

Words by GUS KAHN
Music by FRANK SIGNORELLI and MATT MALNECK

129

I'm In A Minor Key Today

Words and Music by
CHARLOTTE STEINHART and JULES RUBEN

Slowly

Fm7 · Abm/F · Eb/G · F#o · Fm7 · C9

Han-dle me gen-tle treat me right __ Blow my blues a - way __

Fm · Db9 · Gb7-9 · Fm · Db7 · G7(b9) · C7(b9)

I want to lose to - mor - row. __

Bbm7 · Eb7 · Ab

I'm in a min-or key to - day. Lend me your should - er

Fm · G7(b9) · C7 · Db7 · C7 · Fm

© 1987 EMI Music Publishing Ltd., London WC2H 0LD

It Don't Mean A Thing

(If It Ain't Got That Swing)

Words by IRVING MILLS
Music by DUKE ELLINGTON

CHORUS

It's Only A Paper Moon

Words by BILLY ROSE and E. Y. HARBURG
Music by HAROLD ARLEN

It's The Bluest Kind Of Blues

(My Baby Sings)

Words by SPENCER WILLIAMS and JOHN TURNER
Music by DJANGO REINHARDT

CHORUS

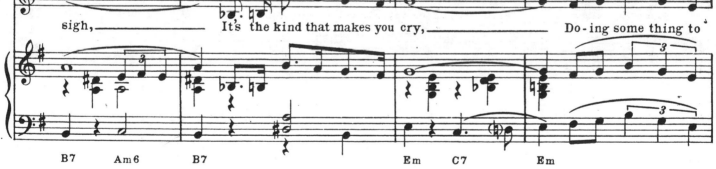

I Wish I Could Shimmy Like
My Sister Kate

Words and Music by ARMAND J. PIRON

CHORUS *Lazily*

Wish I could Shim - my like my sis - ter Kate, She shiv-ers like the Jel - ly

Bb7   F9   Bb7   Eb   Eb7

on a plate;   My mammy want-ed to know last night,

Bb7

Why all the boys treat Sis-ter Kate so nice,   Ev'-ry boy in our

Eb   Ebm Eb   Bb7

neigh-bour hood Knows that she can shimmy and it's un-der - stood.

F7   Bb7   Eb   Eb7

I know I'm late   but I'll   be up to date, When I can shimmy like my sis-ter

Ab   Ebo   Eb   C7   Fm Abm Bb7

1.   2.

Kate.   I Kate, I mean shimmy like my sis-ter Kate._

Eb Bbo Bb7   Eb   C7   Cb7   Bb7   Eb Bb+ Eb

D.S.

Jackass Blues

Words and Music by
ART KASSEL and MEL STITZEL

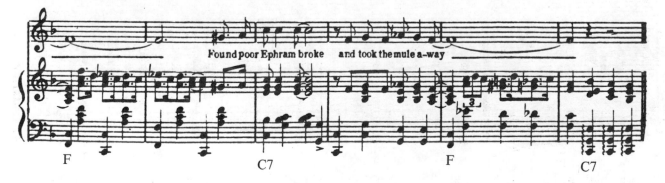

CHORUS

The Japanese Sandman

Words by RAYMOND B. EGAN
Music by RICHARD A. WHITING

Moderato.

VERSE

Won't you stretch im-ag-in-a-tion for the mo-ment and come with
Just as si-lent as we came we'll leave the land of the paint-ed

Fm   Db9   D9

me,......... Let us hast-en to a na-tion ly-ing
fan,......... Wan-der light-ly or you'll wake the lit-tle

C7   Fm

o-ver the west-ern sea;......... Hide be-
peo-ple of old.... Ja-pan;......... May re-

Bbm   G7(b9)   C7

148

CHORUS

Here's the Jap-a-nese Sand - man....... Sneaking on with the dew,.................... Just an old second-

F   D7

-hand   man,............ He'll buy your old day from   you;   He will take eve-ry

G7   C7   F

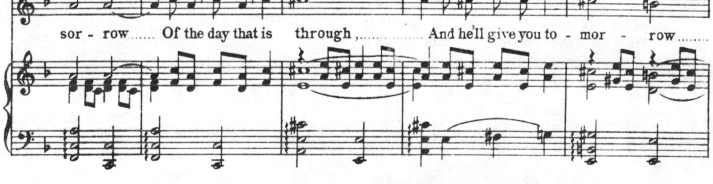

sor - row....... Of the day that is   through ,............... And he'll give you to - mor - row.......

F   A7   E7

.... Just   to start life a - new............................ Then you'll be a bit   old - er.......

A   Aº   Gm7   C7 | F

The Jazz Me Blues

Words and Music by TOM DELANEY

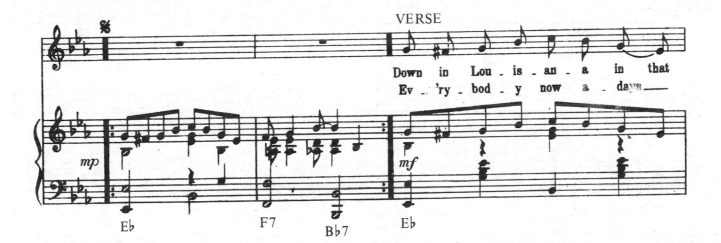

VERSE

Down in Lou_is_an_a in that
Ev_'ry_bod_y now a_days___

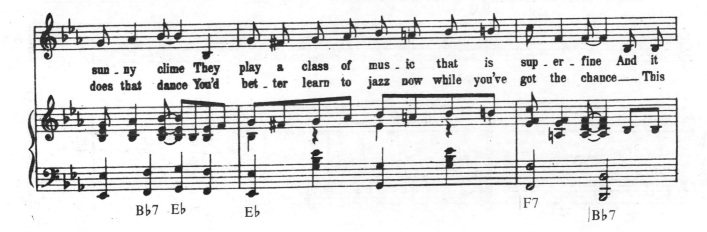

sun_ny clime They play a class of mus_ic that is sup_er_fine And it
does that dance You'd bet_ter learn to jazz now while you've got the chance___ This

noth _ ing else but jazz _ in', jazz _ in' all the time   Ev _ 'ry _ one __ that's nigh
wait _ ing for the time so you can jazz her 'round   Take your time __ and sway,

Eb   Ab   Eb   F7   Bb7 Eb   Bb7

Nev _ er seems __ to sigh   Hear them loud _ ly cry: Oh!
Throw your _ self __ a _ way,   Let me hear you say: Oh!

G°   Bb   Bbm   F7   Bb   G7+

CHORUS

Jazz me __   Come on pro _ fes _ sor and Jazz me __   (Jazz me) You

mf

C7   F7

know I like my jazz _ in' both day and night And if I don't get my jazz _ in' I

Bb7   Eb

don't feel right Now if it's rag _ time please sir will you play it in

F7   Bb7   C7

jazz time _ (Jazz _ time) Don't want it fast Don't want it slow

F7   Eb   G7

Take your time pro _ fes _ sor play it sweet and low I've got those dog _ gone low down

F7   C7   F7   Cm F7

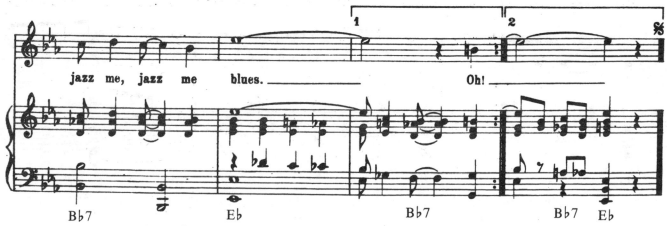

jazz me, jazz me blues. ____ Oh! ____

Bb7   Eb   Bb7   Bb7 Eb

Just A Gigolo

(Schöner Gigolo)

Original German Text by
JULIUS BRAMMER

Words by IRVING CAESAR
Music by LEONELLO CASUCCI

o - ver, and here's how peace had crowned him,___ A few cheap
küs - sen und tan - zen wie kein zwei - ter,___ er kam und

Cm+A   D7   Cm+A   D7   Cm

med - als to wear, and noth - ing more.___ Now ev - 'ry
sah und sieg - te auch im Nu.___ Viel Mon - de

Gm   Eb7   D7   F7

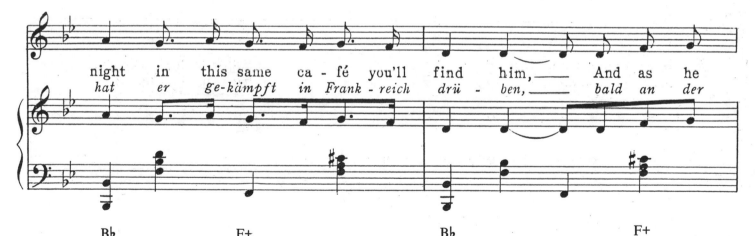

night in this same ca - fé you'll find him,___ And as he
hat er ge - kämpft in Frank - reich drü - ben,___ bald an der

Bb   F+   Bb   F+

strolls by the la - dies hear him say,___ "If you ad - mire me, please
Weich - sel, Pi - a - ve ir - gend - wo.... Jetzt ist ihm nichts mehr ge -

Bb   G7   Cm

hire me, A gi-go-lo who knew a bet-ter day _____
blie - ben, er wur - de Gi - go - lo! _____

Gm   A7   D7   G

REFRAIN

Just A Gi - go - lo,   Ev - 'ry - where I go,
Schö - ner Gi - go - lo,   ar - mer Gi - go - lo,

G

p-f

Peo - ple know the part I'm play - ing,   Paid for ev - 'ry dance,
den - ke nicht mehr an die Zei - ten,   Wo du als Hu - sar,

D7

Sell - ing each ro - mance,   Ev - 'ry night some heart be - tray - ing,
gold - ver-schnürt so-gar,   konn - test durch die Stras - sen rei - ten!

G

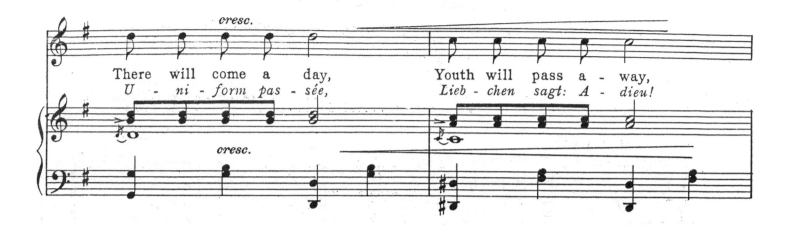

There will come a day,   Youth will pass a - way,
U - ni - form pas - sée,   Lieb - chen sagt: A - dieu!

Then, what will they say   a - bout ___ me,   When the
Schö - ne Welt, du gingst   in Fran - sen!   Wenn das

E7   Am

end comes I know they'll say   "Just A Gi - go - lo,"   As
Herz dir auch bricht, zeig' ein   la - chen - des Ge - sicht,   man

Am7   Cm+A   G   A7

life goes on with - out me. ___   - out me. ___
zahlt und du musst tan - zen! ___   tan - zen!

D7   G   G

Jeepers Creepers

Words by JOHNNY MERCER
Music by HARRY WARREN

wea-ther vane points to gloom-y, It's got-ta be sun-ny
road to com plete dis - as - ter? Each new day I'm fall - in'

to me, When your eyes look in - to mine;
fast - er; You're the rock I per - ish on.

CHORUS

Jeep-ers Creep-ers! Where'd ya get those peep-ers? Jeep-ers Creep-ers!

Where'd ya get those eyes? Gosh all git up! How'd they get so lit up?

Gosh all git up! How'd they get that size? Gol - ly gee!

When you turn those heaters on, Woe is me! Got to put my cheaters on,

Jeep - ers Creep - ers! Where'd ya get those peep - ers? Oh! Those weep - ers!

How they hyp - no - tize!...... Where'd ya get those eyes?... eyes?...

D. C.

Keeps On A Rainin'

Words and Music by
SPENCER WILLIAMS and MAX KORTLANDER

162

Kitchen Man

Words and Music by
ANDY RAZAF and ALEX BELLEDNA

Love Me Or Leave Me

Words by GUS KAHN
Music by WALTER DONALDSON

Chorus-Slowly *(with feeling)*

LOVE ME OR LEAVE ME, and let me be lone-ly;

You won't be-lieve me, and I love you on-ly; I'd rath-er be lone-ly, than

hap-py with some-bod-y else. _____ You might find the night-time, the

right time for kiss-ing; But night-time is my time for just rem-i-nis-cing, Re-

gret-ting, in-stead of for-get-ting with some-bod-y else. _____

There'll be no - one un - less that some-one is you;

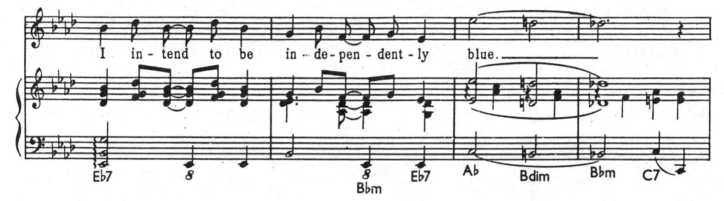

I in - tend to be in - de - pen - dent - ly blue.

I want your love, but I don't want to bor - row, To have it to-day, and to

give back to - mor - row; For my love is your love, there's no love for no-bod-y else!

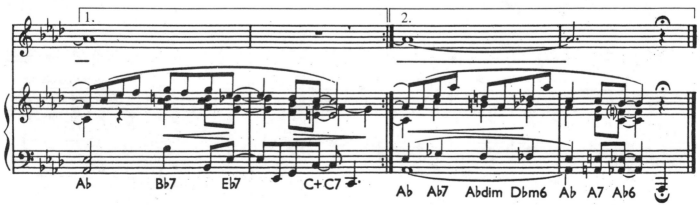

Lulu's Back In Town

Words by AL DUBIN
Music by HARRY WARREN

look my best,... Lu-lu's back in town;............ Gotta get a half-a-buck some-where, gotta shine my shoes and

slick my hair, Got-ta get my-self a bou-ton-niere,... Lu-lu's back in town.......... You can tell all my

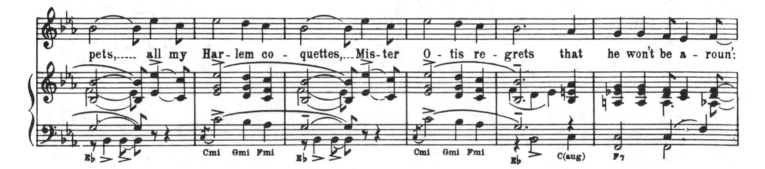

pets,..... all my Har-lem co-quettes,...Mis-ter O-tis re-grets that he won't be a-roun':

.... You can tell the mail-man not to call,... I ain't com-in' home un-til the fall...And I

might not get back home at all,... Lu-lu's back in town.................. ....

Mama's Gone, Good-bye

Words and Music by
PETER BOCAGE and A. J. PIRON

174

I ain't no fool _____ I'm goin' to

get a man to treat me right ___ One who'll stay home

D7

G7   C7

ev'-ry night Fare thee well _____ Ma ma's, gone, good-

Bb   Gb   F7

1 - bye _____ 2 Fare thee well bye _____

Bb   Bb   F7+ Bb

Milenberg Joys

Words by WALTER MELROSE
Music by FERD 'JELLY ROLL' MORTON/PAUL MARES/LEON ROPPOLO

Moanin' Low

Words by HOWARD DIETZ
Music by RALPH RAINGER

Messin' Around

Words and Music by
JOHN A. ST. CYR and CHARLES L. COOKE

What is all this noise I hear a-round here?_____ Please don't keep me in doubt;
Dad-dy spent the night down in a ca - fé,_____ Came home at break of day;

What is it all a - bout? Now, Hon-ey calm your-self and don't be an-gry with me,_____
Oh, boy! how he did sway! Then ma-ma met him at the door with freez-in'-est bow,_____

And right here on this spot, 'Some-thing hot you'll see! _____
And said, "Dog-gone your soul, Get me told right now"! _____

C   F#7   C   B7   E   B7   G7

CHORUS

That dance called "Mess-in' A - round," A dance that's new in the town;
Have you been "Mess-in' A - round," Have you been paintin' the town:

p-f

C   F7

It runs the Charles-ton way out of gas. _____ Don't
'Cause if you were, you can catch some air. _____ I

C   Ab7   Db

e - ven have to step, and still it's full of pep; Keep your dog-gies still,
tried to use you right, but you stayed out all night; 'Spose you got a thrill,

A7   D7

Mood Indigo

Words and Music by
DUKE ELLINGTON, IRVING MILLS and ALBANY BIGARD

CHORUS

Al-ways get that mood in-di-go,__ Since my ba-by said good - bye,

Ab   Ab° Ab   Bb7   Bbm   Eb7   Ab G Bb7 Eb7

In the eve - nin' when lights are low,__ I'm so lone-some I could cry,

Ab   Bb7   Eb7

'Cause there's no-bo-dy who cares a-bout me,__ I'm just a soul who's blu-er than blue can be,

Ab7   Db7   Eb7

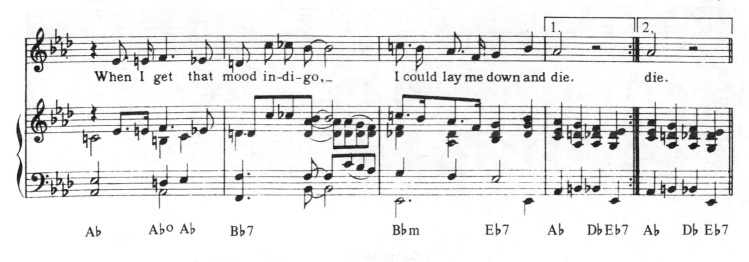

When I get that mood in-di-go,__ I could lay me down and die.   die.

Ab   Ab° Ab   Bb7   Bbm   Eb7   Ab Db Eb7 Ab Db Eb7

Moonburn

Words by EDWARD HEYMAN
Music by HOAGY CARMICHAEL

Moderato

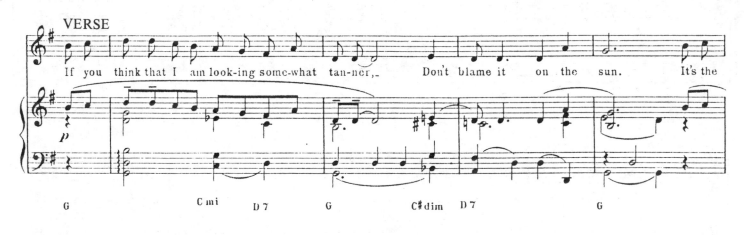

VERSE

If you think that I am look-ing some-what tan-ner,_ Don't blame it on the sun. It's the

G   C mi   D 7   G   C#dim   D 7   G

moon-light and the sweet-ness in your man-ner_ That makes me the health-y one. When the

C mi   D7   G   C#dim   D 7   G

moon hangs low   I be-gin to glow   And my day has just be - gun.___

D   A7   D   Emi 7   A7   D   Emi7   E 7   A7   D7

CHORUS

I'm gon-na get a moon-burn When I'm with you to - night, So ve-ry

soon I'll moon-burn When you hold me tight. I'll ask the glowing stars up a-bove me What your

lips will im-part, And when they flash, the word that you love me, It will warm my

heart! I'll get a brand new moon-burn With ev-'ry kiss from you, And if I

have my way, If I can have my say, You'll get a moon - burn too! I'm gon-na too!

Mouthful O' Jam

Words by JOHNNY MERCER
Music by ARCHIE BLEYER

mouth - ful o' jam.___
right to the grave.___

Db7   C7 Fm   Fm   Gm7   Fm   C7

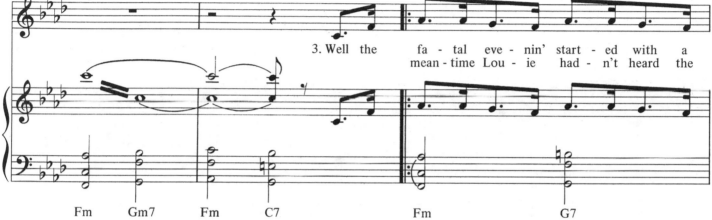

3. Well the fa - tal eve - nin' start - ed with a
mean - time Lou - ie had - n't heard the

Fm   Gm7   Fm   C7   Fm   G7

par - ty,   And the pro - gramme was - n't meant to be hot___ But it
shoot - in'   He was sleep - in' like an in - no - cent lamb___   When he

Fm   C7   Fm   G7   Fm   C7

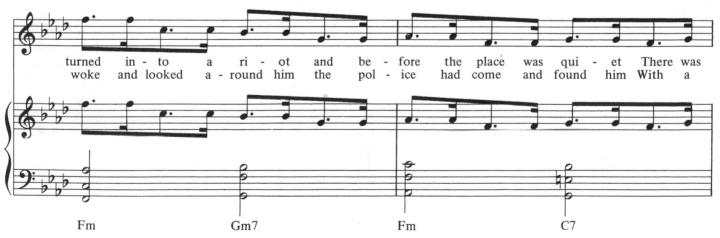

turned in - to a ri - ot and be - fore the place was qui - et There was
woke and looked a - round him the pol - ice had come and found him With a

Fm   Gm7   Fm   C7

My Baby Just Cares For Me

Words by GUS KAHN
Music by WALTER DONALDSON

© 1930 Bregman Vocco & Conn Inc., USA
Sub-published by Francis Day & Hunter Ltd./EMI Music Publishing Ltd., London WC2H 0LD

CHORUS

My Melancholy Baby

Words by GEORGE A. NORTON
Music by ERNIE BURNETT

1. Come, sweet-heart mine Don't sit and pine—
2. Birds in the trees, Sweet mel - o - dies—

Tell me of the cares that make you feel so blue What have I done?
They will take you to a land of peace-ful dreams Clouds will roll by—

CHORUS Slowly (with feeling)

Come to me, my mel-an-cho-ly ba — by Cud-dle up and don't be blue___

All your fears are fool-ish fan-cy may be You know, dear, that I'm in love with

you___ Ev-'ry cloud must have a sil-ver lin — ing Wait un-til the

sun shines through___ Smile, my hon-ey dear While I kiss a-way each tear Or

else I shall be mel-an-cho-ly, too. too.

There Is
No Greater Love

Words by MARTY SYMES
Music by ISHAM JONES

CHORUS

There is No GREAT-ER LOVE than what I feel for you, _____

C   F   E+

_____ No GREAT-ER LOVE, _____ no heart so true. _____ There is no

E   A7   D7   G7

great-er thrill than what you bring to me, _____ No sweet-er

C   F   E+   E   A7

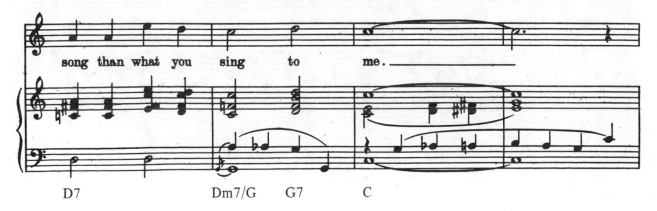

song than what you sing to me. _____

D7   Dm7/G   G7   C

You're the sweet-est thing   I have ev-er known,   And to think that

E7   Am   E7   Am   E

you are mine a - lone!   There is No GREAT-ER LOVE in

Am   D7   G   C

all   the world, it's   true,   No GREAT-ER   LOVE than what I

F   E+   E   A7   D7

1.   **2.**

feel   for   you.   There is No   you.

Dm7/G G7   C   A♭7   G   C   Fm6   C

On Green Dolphin Street

Words by NED WASHINGTON
Music by BRONISLAU KAPER

203

On The Alamo

Words by GUS KAHN and JOE LYONS
Music by ISHAM JONES

CHORUS

Where the moon swings low_____ On the Al - a - mo_____ In a gar-den

Eb   F7

fair,   where ros - es grow_____   In the ten - der

Bb7   Eb   Bb7 Fm7/Bb

light_____   of the sum-mer night._____   I can see her wan - der

Eb   Gm   Cm Gm Bb7

to   and fro_____   For she said "I'll wait_____   By the gar - den

F7   Bb7   Tacit   Eb

gate" _____ On the night I said "I love you

F7

so" _____ And in all my dreams it seems, I

Eb   Cm

go _____ Where the moon swings low On the

Aº   Tacit   F7   Bb7

1 Al - a - mo. _____ Where the moon swings Al - a - mo. _____

Eb   Bb7 Fm7   Eb

On The Old Dominion Line

Words by JEAN C. HAVEZ
Music by GEORGE BOTSFORD

CHORUS

On the Old Do - min-ion Line _____ as the stars a - bove us

Bb C7 F7

shine, _____ Ho-ney it's sweet _ when we are hum-ming a song _

Bb F7

steam-ing a - long _ dream-ing a-long _ Put your head right close to

Bb

mine _____ so I'll see the love-light shine _____

C7 F7 D

Au - to - mo - bi - ling ain't as jol - ly as this ____

G7   C7

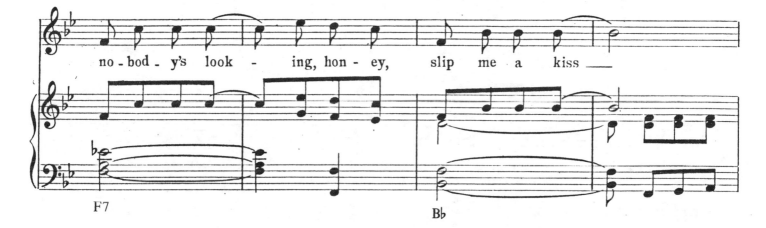

no - bod - y's look - ing, hon - ey, slip me a kiss ____

F7   Bb

This is the life ____ for us it's cer - tain - ly bliss ____ on the

C7

Old Do - min - ion Line.   On the Line. ____ D.C.

Bb   Cm / F7 / Bb   F7   Bb / / F7 Bb

Poor Butterfly

Words by JOHN L. GOLDEN
Music by RAYMOND HUBBELL

214

CHORUS
Slowly with much expression.

Papa-De-Da-Da

Words and Music by
CLARENCE TODD, SPENCER WILLIAMS and CLARENCE WILLIAMS

Rose Room

New Words and Music by
CHRIS ELLIS and CECIL BOLTON

'Round Midnight

Words by BERNIE HANIGHEN
Music by COOTIE WILLIAMS and THELONIOUS MONK

San

Words and Music by
LINDSAY McPHAIL and WALTER MICHELS

Chorus

Oh, sweet-heart Lo - na, My dar-ling Lo - na, Why have you gone a - way? ___
Oh, sweet-heart Lo - na, My dar-ling Lo - na, Have you come back to stay? ___

___ You said you loved me, But if you loved me Why did you act this
___ You said you loved me, I knew you loved me, I knew you'd come some

way? ___ If I had ev-er been un-true to you What you have
day. ___ If I had ev-er been un-true to you What you have

done would be the thing to do. But my heart aches, dear, And it will
done would be the thing to do. But now you're mine, dear, For all the

break, dear, If you don't come back home a-gain to San.
time, dear, And you're for-giv-en by your lov-ing San.

Stella By Starlight

Words by NED WASHINGTON
Music by VICTOR YOUNG

VERSE

Have you seen Stel-la by star-light, Stand-ing a-lone,

moon in her hair? Have you seen Stel-la by star-light,

When have you known rap-ture so rare?

CHORUS **Moderato**

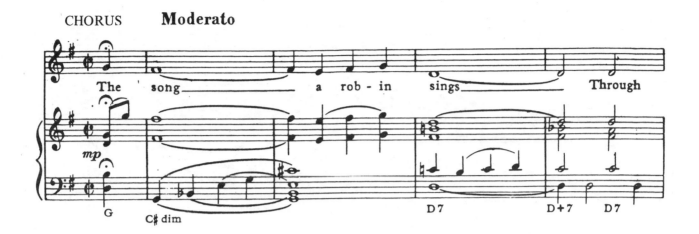

The song _____ a rob - in sings _____ Through

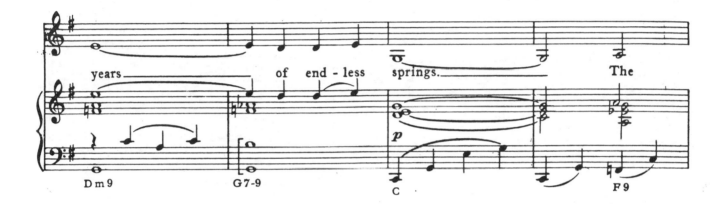

years _____ of end - less springs. _____ The

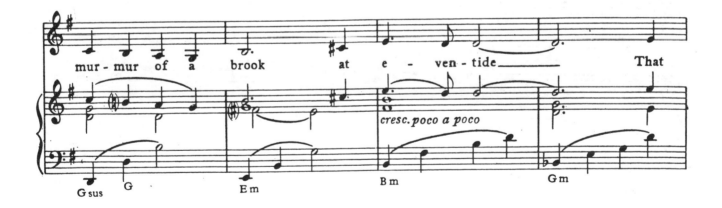

mur - mur of a brook at e - ven - tide _____ That

rip - ples by a nook _____ where two lov - ers hide. _____ A

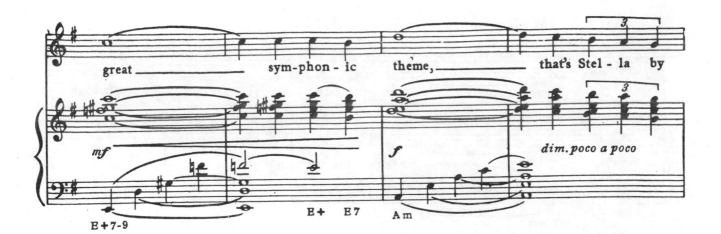

great _____ sym-phon-ic theme, _____ that's Stel-la by

E+7-9   E+   E7   Am

star light _____ and not a dream. _____   *(BOY)* My
                                                          (GIRL) She's

Cm   G

heart _____   and I a - gree _____ She's ev - 'ry-
all _____   of these and more _____ She's ev - 'ry-

C# dim   Dm   E7

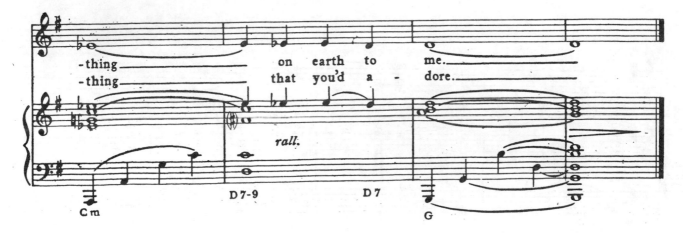

-thing _____   on earth to me. _____
-thing _____   that you'd a - dore. _____

rall.

Cm   D7-9   D7   G

Stormy Weather

(Keeps Rainin' All The Time)

Words by TED KOEHLER
Music by HAROLD ARLEN

Life is bare, _____ gloom and mis - 'ry ev - 'ry - where, Storm - y

Db   Eb7   Ab   Adim   Db   Eb7

weath-er, _____ Just can't get my poor self to - ge - ther, _____ I'm wea-ry all_ the

Ab   Db   Eb7   Ab   Db   Eb+

time, _____ the time, _____ So wea-ry all_ the time, _____

Ab   Db   Ab Adim   Db   Eb+   Ab

When he went a - way_ the blues walk'd in   and met me, _____ If   he stays a - way_ old rock - in'
(she)   (she)

Db   Ab   Db

chair will get me, All I do is pray the Lord a - bove will let me_ walk in the sun once

Ab   Db   Ab   Db   Ab   Db   Ab   Ab   F7

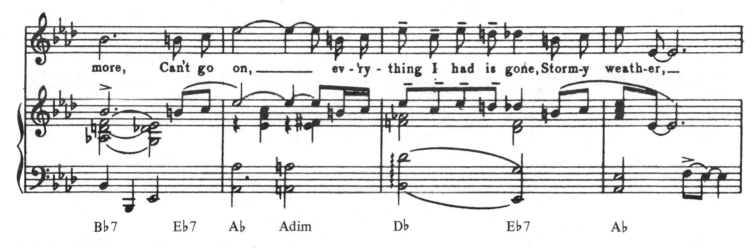

more, Can't go on,____ ev-'ry-thing I had is gone, Storm-y weath-er,____

Bb7   Eb7   Ab   Adim   Db   Eb7   Ab

Since my man and I ____ ain't to-geth-er,____ Keeps rain-in' all the time,____
(gal)

Db   Eb7   Ab   Db   Eb+   Ab

1   **2**

Keeps rain-in' all_ the time.____   Don't know time.____

Db   Eb+   Ab   Db   Eb7   Ab   Bbm Ab Db Ab

pp

Strut Miss Lizzie

Words and Music by
HENRY CREAMER and TURNER LAYTON

CHORUS

234

PATTER. (*ad lib*) *To follow 1st Chorus after 2nd Verse*

Go down the street   by the school   Pat your feet you   step-pin' fool   Strut your stuff,

Gb7 / Bb / Gb7 / Bb / Gb7 Bb / / C7 / F7 / Gb7 / Bb

use your brain, trot your tootsies down the lane;   Thru the al-ley   dodge the cans, Shake Miss Sally's

Gb7 / Bb / Bb D7 Abo G7 C7 F7 Bb / Gb7 / Bb / Gb7 / Bb / Gb7 Bb / /

pots and pans   Pull yourself to - gether   now we're going to have a   real "Tow Row" Won't you

C7 / F7 / Bb / Bb7 / Eb / Gb7 / Bb   C7 F7   Bb Bb7

Sweet Georgia Brown

Words and Music by
MACEO PINKARD, KEN CASEY and BEN BERNIE

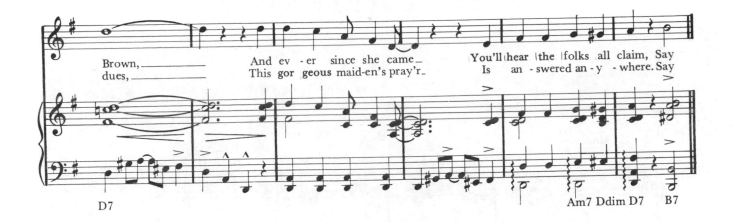

Brown,_____ And ev - er since she came_ You'll hear the folks all claim, Say
dues,_____ This gor geous maid-en's pray'r_ Is an - swered an - y - where. Say

D7
Am7 Ddim D7   B7

CHORUS

No gal made_ has got the shade_ On sweet Geor-gia Brown,_

E7

Two left feet,_ but, oh! so neat_ has sweet Geor-gia Brown._ They all sigh_ and

A7
D7

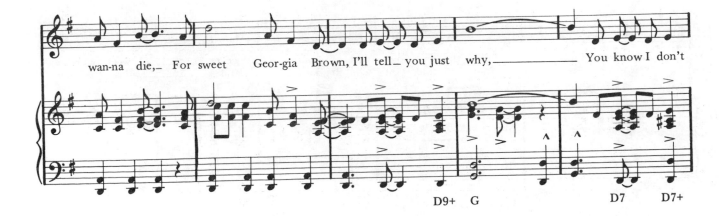

wan-na die,_ For sweet Geor-gia Brown, I'll tell_ you just why,_____ You know I don't

D9+ G
D7   D7+

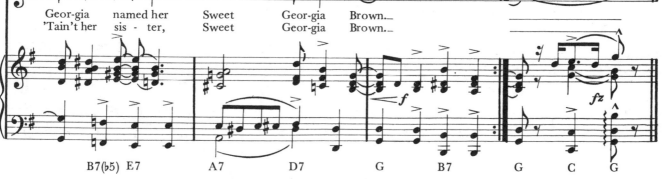

Sweet Honey Will Be Gone

TRAD: New Words & Musical Adaptation by
CHRIS ELLIS & CECIL BOLTON

I'm tired of fuss-in' and call-in' you down

Your trif-lin' ways are the talk of the town

You've run a-round and tried to two time me.

Caused me lots of mis-er-y_____ Done ev' - ry -

F7   Bb7   Eb

thing that a sweet dad - dy should _ Done ev' - ry - thing I

Bb7   Eb   Eb7

could. _____ And still you don't ap - pre - ci - ate _

Ab   C7/G   Bb   G7
              F7

_ Soon it's gon - na be to late. _____ You're

Cm7   F7   Fm7/Bb   Bb

CHORUS

gon - na wake some morn - in' and find your - self in mourn - in'

Eb   Ab9

Your sweet hon - ey will be gone _____ You're gon - na wake up

Eb   Bb7   Eb   Eb

cry - in' And you're gon - na wake up sigh - in' You're gon - na

Ab7   F7

feel your life is done. _____ Re - mem - ber you

Bb7   Eb

Them There Eyes

Words and Music by
DORIS TAUBER, WILLIAM TRACEY and MACEO PINKARD

There Ain't No Sweet Man
That's Worth The Salt Of My Tears

Words and Music by
FRED FISHER

That Da-Da Strain

Words and Music by
J. EDGAR DOWELL and MAMIE MEDINA

248

Too Broken Hearted To Cry

(Bix's Blues)

New Words and Music by
CHRIS ELLIS and CECIL BOLTON
(Based on a Theme by BIX BEIDERBECKE)

Won't you hur - ry back a - gain ___

F   A7

'Fore I pine a - way and die ___ I ___ have got the sad old blues ___

Bb   Gm7

1.
much to bro - ken heart - ed to cry. ___

C7   F   Gm7   F   Gm

2.
much to bro - ken heart - ed to cry. ___

C7   Eb9   F6/9

Truckin' On Down

Words by ARTHUR PORTER
Music by EUBIE BLAKE

All the high brows shout_____ when the M. C. hol-lers out.

CHORUS

Truck on down,_____   Truck on down,_____

Get the mo-tion first then you run a - muck. You have-n't done a thing_ un-til you

learn to truck_ It's ea - sy stick a - round,_____   Stick a - round,_____

Washboard Blues

Words and Music by
HOAGY CARMICHAEL, IRVING MILLS and F. CALLAHAN

1. Morn - in' comes with cloud - y skies and rain, Mah po' back is broke with pain,
2. Wash - in' in a shan - ty on de sho', Riv - ah swing - in' on by de do',

My man's sleep - in', I'se a scrub - bin', Chil - lin' weep - in', I'se a rub - bin'
Heah de riv - ah low - ly call - in', I'm a - shiv - ah night a fall - in'

Pain a - creep - in', cloes a - tub - bin, WASH - BOARD BLUES.
Heah de riv - ah low - ly moan - in', WASH - BOARD BLUES.

CHORUS

PATTER

CHORUS

The Way I Feel Today

Words by ANDY RAZAF
Music by DONALD REDMAN and HOWARD QUICKSELL

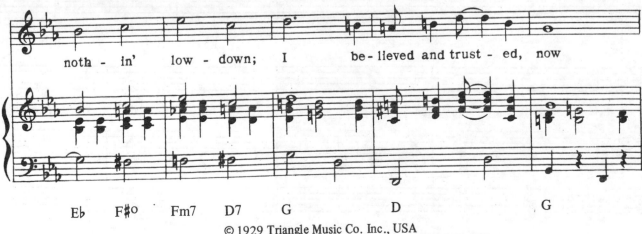

I'm dis - gust - ed, I found him out,— at the show— down:

Bb7   Cm   Gm7   Fm7/B   Bb7

Chorus

When I think of him, how much I love him, I get a des - per - ate

Eb   Bb7   Eb   Bb7   Eb F#o   Bb7

no - tion, That's THE WAY I FEEL TO - DAY; My

Eb D7 Eb Cm7 B7 Bb7 Eb   Fm7   Bb7

heart is break - in', be - cause he's mak - in', a play-thing of my de - vo - tion,

Eb   Bb7   Eb   Bb7   Eb F#o Bb7 Eb D7

261

262

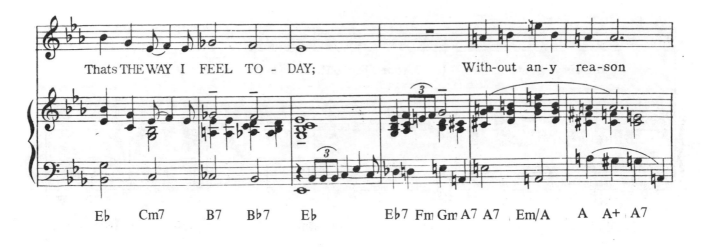

What's New?

Words by JOHNNY BURKE
Music by BOB HAGGART

How did that romance come through?............ We have-n't met since

then, Gee! but it's nice to see you a - gain.

What's new?........ Prob-ab-ly I'm bor-ing you,

But see-ing you is grand,

When Lights Are Low

Words by SPENCER WILLIAMS
Music by BENNY CARTER

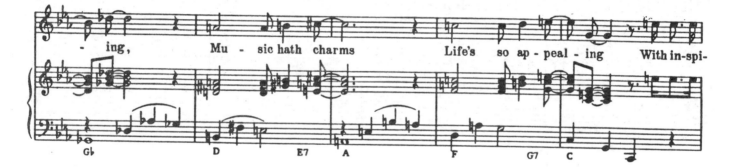

When Your Lover Has Gone

Words and Music by
E. A. SWANN

The mag-ic moon-light dies. At break of dawn, There is no sun-rise,

When your lov-er has gone. What lone-ly

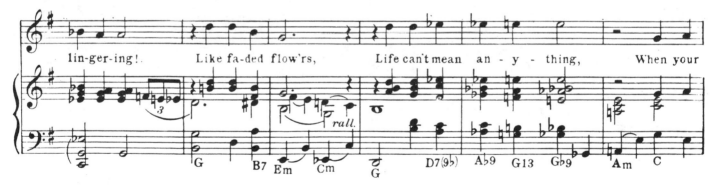

hours The eve-ning shad-ows bring! What lone-ly hours With mem'ries

lin-ger-ing! Like fa-ded flow'rs, Life can't mean an-y-thing, When your

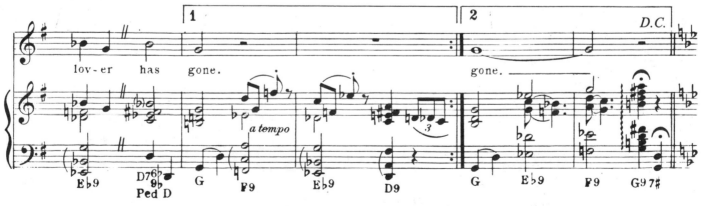

lov-er has gone. gone.

Whispering

Words by JOHN SCHONBERGER
Music by MALVIN SCHONBERGER

CHORUS *2nd time*

When Somebody Thinks You're Wonderful

Words and Music by HARRY WOODS

© 1935 M. Witmark & Sons, USA
Sub-published by B. Feldman & Co. Ltd., London WC2H 0LD

274

When You're Smiling

(The whole world smiles with you)

Words by JOE GOODWIN and MARK FISHER
Music by LARRY SHAY

276

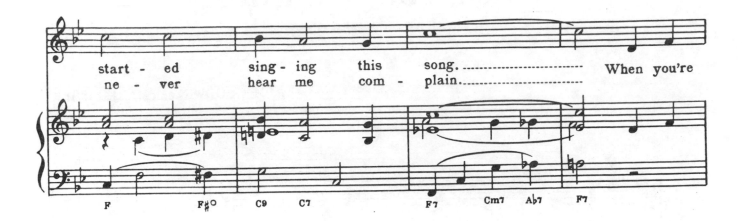

CHORUS

Who'll Chop Your Suey When I'm Gone

Words by ROUSSEAU SIMMONS
Music by SIDNEY BECHET

© 1925 Clarence Williams Music Publishing Co., USA
Sub-published by B. Feldman & Co. Ltd., London WC2H 0LD

Who'll clam your chow-der Fri - day night?_____ 1. Who'll tute your
2. Who'll bake your

G C / Cm G C9 G7

fruit - i home just right?_____
Jel - ly roll just right?_____ Tell me while I'm

/ / / G+5 C Co / / C A9

put - ting Chi - li in your con - carne, Who'll Chop your

D G6 F#7 Fmaj7 E7 Am7

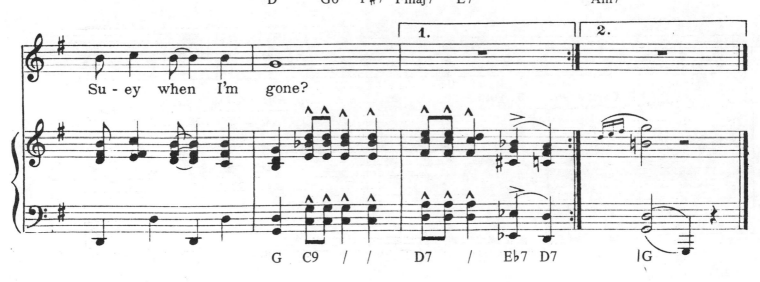

1. **2.**

Su - ey when I'm gone?

G C9 / / D7 / Eb7 D7 |G

Who Broke The Lock Off The Hen House Door

By HENRY TROY & SNEEZE WILLIAMS

VOICE

I'm on my rounds____ go - ing____
I just got back____ from____

ev - e - ry where ____ Just got a trip ____ scand - al's
Tenn - es - see ____ They tho't I was the man ____ so they

must find out ___ be - fore I go ___ Who in the

heck broke the lock off the hen house door. ___ Tell me hen house door. ___

3. Brother Henry Barkesdade in the grave yard one night
   Searching for the man but saw a form in white
   Henry having only one leg was in dutch
   You should have seen him run when he threw 'way his crutch.

4. The dogs found a scent which led to a tree
   Elder Brown said "If he's up there he belongs to me"
   Elder climbed the tree but found 't'was a bear
   They clinched, Elder yelled "Lemme down for air."

5. Brother Lemon Coleman, deacon of the church,
   Was openly accused by ole sister Burch
   He pleaded not guilty had a good alibi
   Was stealing pigs that night from the Elder's sty.

6. You've heard the question now I'll leave you flat
   It's an old, old story you can bet on that
   It sounds a little fishy it surely isn't new
   The answer to it all, I'm leaving up to you.

Willow, Weep For Me

Words and Music by
ANN RONELL

1. Oh, Lord, _____ why did you send the dark-ness to me? _____
2. Oh, Lord, _____ is that sweet spell of rap-ture di - vine, _____

A+   D9   G9   C9

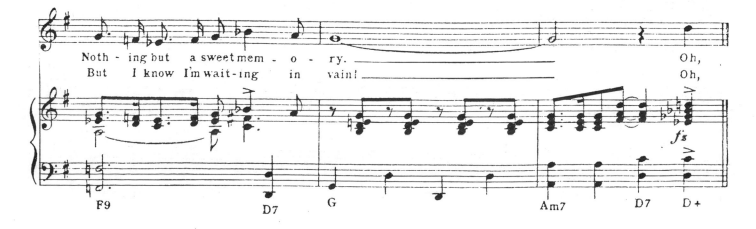

You Must Have Been A Beautiful Baby

Words by JOHNNY MERCER
Music by HARRY WARREN

Your Feets Too Big

Words and Music by
ADA BENSON and FRED FISHER

You're Gonna Hate Yourself
(In The Morning)

Words and Music by
BOB MUSEL and WALLY RIDLEY

never - er could be hap - py with some - one new____ 'Cos
keep for - get - ting some - thing I want to hear____ and

Ab

Eb7

we be - long to - geth - er hon - ey you know it's true____ You're gon - na
nows the time to say it ba - by loud and clear____ You're gon - na

Ab

Db7

Eb7

hate your - self in the morn - ing____ If you
hate your - self in the morn - ing____ If you

Ab

Bbm

Ab

F7

don't say "I love__ you" to - night____ You're gon - na
don't say "I love__ you" to - night.

Bb

Eb13

Ab

Ab

You're My Thrill

Lyrics by SIDNEY CLARE
Music by JAY GORNEY

Slowly, with feeling

VERSE

I've been 'neath the moon be-fore held by the charms of oth-er arms I heard love's old tune be-fore And it used to bore me 'till you stood be-fore me.

CHORUS

YOU'RE MY THRILL, you do some-thing to me, You send chills right

through me, When I look at you 'cause you're my thrill, YOU'RE MY THRILL,

how my pulse in-creas-es, I just go to piec-es, When I look at you 'cause

you're my thrill. Hm_____ No-thing seems to mat-ter,

Hm _____ Here's my heart on a sil - ver plat - ter, where's my

E7 Arit.　E7　Bm75♮　E7　A7　B♭7　A♭7　A7

will?　Why this strange de - sire?　That keeps mount-ing high-er,

Em75♭　A7　Em7 5♭　A7　Cm　Am75♭　D7

When I look at you I can't keep still, YOU'RE MY

G7　E♭9　Dm　B♭7　Dm　Dm7　G7　Gm6

1　2

THRILL. _____　THRILL. _____

D　B♭7　D　D　A♭9　D6

You've Got The Right Key
But The Wrong Keyhole

Words & Music by
EDDIE GREEN & CLARENCE WILLIAMS

clock   He tried his key in the old front door___ but the key would-n't fit the lock___

A7   G7   C   A7   Dm   G7

___   He pushed it in___ and turned it   round   and round then pulled it   out___

C   Dm C   G7

___   And   just as he was a-bout to try a-gain   he heard Miss Li - za shout. "You've got the

C   G7   C

CHORUS

right   key but the wrong key-hole.   I could-n't get a-long with you to save   my soul.___ Now

D7   G7

Printed by Loader Jackson Printers Arlesey Beds 3/90